Let's Drum!

Description

After reading an inspiring true story about a young female drummer, students explore the phenomenon that different kinds of drums make different sounds. They learn about the basic parts of a drum, how drums make sound, and that repeated sound patterns are called *rhythms*. Students design and build their own drums out of everyday items, explain how they make sound, and create their own rhythms using their handmade drums.

Alignment With the *Next Generation Science Standards*

Performance Expectations

1-PS4-1: Plan and conduct investigations to provide evidence that vibrating materials can make sound and that sound can make materials vibrate.

K-2-ETS1-2: Develop a simple sketch, drawing, or physical model to illustrate how the shape of an object helps it function as needed to solve a given problem.

Science and Engineering Practices	Disciplinary Core Ideas	Crosscutting Concepts
Constructing Explanations and Designing Solutions Use tools and/or materials to design and/or build a device that solves a specific problem or a solution to a specific problem. **Obtaining, Evaluating, and Communicating Information** Read grade-appropriate texts and/or use media to obtain scientific and/or technical information to determine patterns in and/or evidence about the natural and designed world(s). Communicate information or design ideas and/or solutions with others in oral and/or written forms using models, drawings, writing, or numbers that provide detail about scientific ideas, practices, and/or design ideas.	**PS4.A: Wave Properties** Sound can make matter vibrate, and vibrating matter can make sound. **ETS1.B: Developing Possible Solutions** Designs can be conveyed through sketches, drawings, or physical models. These representations are useful in communicating ideas to a problem's solutions to other people.	**Patterns** Patterns in the natural and human designed world can be observed, used to describe phenomena, and used as evidence. **Scale, Proportion, and Quantity** Relative scales allow objects and events to be compared and described (e.g., bigger and smaller, hotter and colder, faster and slower.)

Note: The activities in this lesson will help students move toward the performance expectations listed, which is the goal after multiple activities. However, the activities will not by themselves be sufficient to reach the performance expectations.

Featured Picture Books

TITLE: ***Drum Dream Girl: How One Girl's Courage Changed Music***
AUTHOR: **Margarita Engle**
ILLUSTRATOR: **Rafael López**
PUBLISHER: **HMH Books for Young Readers**
YEAR: **2015**
GENRE: **Story**
SUMMARY: *Engle's beautiful, rhythmic poem tells the story of Millo Castro Zaldarriaga, a Chinese-African-Cuban girl who broke Cuba's traditional taboo against female drummers. It is an inspiring true story for dreamers everywhere.*

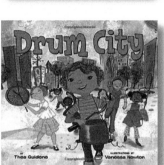

TITLE: ***Drum City***
AUTHOR: **Thea Guidone**
ILLUSTRATOR: **Vanessa Newton**
PUBLISHER: **Dragonfly Books**
YEAR: **2010**
GENRE: **Poetry**
SUMMARY: *A young boy begins banging on pots and pans in his front yard, enticing other children to join him. Before long, the entire city is feeling the beat.*

Time Needed

This lesson will take several class periods. Suggested scheduling is as follows:

Session 1: **Engage** with *Drum Dream Girl* Read-Aloud and **Explore** with Different Drums, Different Sounds

Session 2: **Explain** with Drum Sounds Article

Session 3: **Elaborate** with *Drum City* Read-Aloud

Session 4: **Evaluate** with My Drum Design

Materials

Per class

- World map or globe

For Different Drums, Different Sounds

- 3 or more different types of drums, such as congas, bongos, timbales, snares, hand drums, and tubanos (Check with your school music teacher, high school band director, or local music school about borrowing drums and possibly connecting you with a guest drummer for this activity.)
- Clean cylindrical containers (with any sharp edges covered with duct tape or masking tape), such as the following:

- Coffee cans
- Popcorn tins
- Cookie tins
- Oatmeal containers
- Plastic butter containers
- Items to use as drumsticks, such as the following:
    - Real wooden drumsticks (You can usually purchase inexpensive wooden drumsticks online for less than $1 each.)
    - Chopsticks
    - Dowel rods
    - Wooden spoons
    - Pencils

For Drum Sounds Article's Stop-and-Try-It Activities

- Drumstick
- Drum (any type)
- Large bowl
- Plastic wrap
- Large rubber band or tape to attach plastic wrap to bowl
- 1 teaspoon dry rice grains or sprinkles

For My Drum Design

- Containers and items to use as drumsticks from earlier activities
- Materials to make drumheads, such as the following:
    - Duct tape
    - Packing tape
    - Heat-activated shrink wrap
    - Large balloons (non-latex)
    - Large rubber bands or tape
    - Glue
- Art supplies to cover and decorate the drum shells, such as the following:
    - Construction paper
    - Markers
    - Crayons
    - Stickers
    - Patterned duct tape
    - Glitter glue

SAFETY

- Use safety glasses or goggles when constructing drums.
- Be sure that containers used did not previously hold food allergens (e.g., peanuts and tree nuts).
- Dowels, chopsticks, and so forth are considered potential sharps and impalement hazards. Students should be cautioned about their use and should use them only under direct adult supervision.
- Use caution when handling metal cans. The lips of cans can be sharp and cut skin. Remind students not to remove tape.
- Remind students to quickly pick up any spilled rice grains on the floor—they are a potential slip/fall hazard.
- Have students wash hands with soap and water after completing activities.

Background for Teachers

Sound is a form of energy caused by vibrations. If you hum and hold your fingers on the front of your neck, you can feel your vocal cords rapidly moving back and forth. These vibrations also cause particles of air around them to vibrate. Sounds need a medium to travel through. Most of the sounds we hear are traveling through air, but sound can also travel through solids and liquids. Some materials are better at carrying sounds than others. Sound travels fastest through solids, slower through liquids, and slowest through gases. *Volume* is the measure of how loud or soft a sound is. Volume is measured in decibels (dB). *Pitch* is the measure of how high or low a sound is and is determined by the rate of vibrations: The higher the rate of vibration, or *frequency*, the higher the pitch. Music is defined as the ordering of sounds to produce a composition having unity and continuity. Music can be created by voices or instruments, each producing sound in different ways.

The drum is probably the world's oldest musical instrument, yet the basic design has remained virtually unchanged to this day. A drum has three main parts: the head, rim, and shell. The *head* of a drum is the part that is struck with hands, sticks, or mallets. A drumhead is sometimes referred to as a *skin* because, for a long time, drumheads were made from stretched animal skins. Today, most drumheads are made of a synthetic polymer. The *rim* of a drum is the edge around the head. Drummers can play the rim of the drum to get a sound that is different from playing on the head. The *shell* of a drum is the part that has the head stretched over it. Most drum shells are wooden and have a cylindrical or truncated cone shape. However, some shells are bowl-shaped, such as timpani, and some are even six-sided and box-shaped.

A cylindrical shape helps the sound reverberate evenly inside the enclosed space when the drummer hits the drumhead, giving a fuller, richer sound. It is also easier to stretch a drumhead over a round shape than a rectangular or irregular shape. When a drumhead is struck, it *vibrates*, or moves up and down very quickly. The sound waves caused by the vibrations travel in all directions. When they reach your ears, you hear the drum. All sounds are caused by vibrations. The sound of a drum is affected by the size, shape, thickness, and material of the shell; the material and tightness of the head; and the object used to strike the drum. The sound can also be changed depending on where you hit the drum. Drums are typically played on their heads, but a drummer can also strike the rim or shell to add different sounds.

The difference between making noise on a drum and making music on a drum has to do with patterns. A drummer can keep a steady beat, or an unchanging tempo of a musical piece, but to really make music, a drummer also uses repeated patterns of sound called *rhythms*. A simple way to teach the concept of rhythm is to have students tap or clap out the rhythm of simple nursery rhymes. For example, clapping out each syllable of "Hickory Dickory Dock" (Hick/o/ry Dick/o/ry Dock) establishes a simple pattern that can be repeated to form a rhythm. The addition of sound patterns to make rhythms is just one example of how mathematics and music are related.

In this lesson, students are introduced to the concept that vibrating materials make sound and sound can make materials vibrate. Then they apply their knowledge of how drums make sound by making

their own drums out of everyday materials. This activity incorporates the science and engineering practice (SEP) of designing solutions. Students not only explore how drums make sound but also learn how music is made on drums by using repeated patterns of sound. The SEP of obtaining, evaluating, and communicating information is used as students make sense of their observations by reading a nonfiction article about drums and sound. The crosscutting concept (CCC) of patterns is reinforced by students' creating rhythms on their own drums, and the CCC of scale, proportion, and quantity is explored as students use words like *bigger, smaller, louder,* and *softer* to compare drums and the sounds they make.

Learning Progressions

Below are the disciplinary core idea (DCI) grade band endpoints for grades K–2 and 3–5. These are provided to show how student understanding of the DCIs in this lesson will progress in future grade levels.

DCIs	Grades K–2	Grades 3–5
PS4.A: Wave Properties	• Sound can make matter vibrate and vibrating matter can make sound.	• Waves of the same type can differ in amplitude (height of the wave) and wavelength (spacing between the wave peaks).
ETS1.B: Developing Possible Solutions	• Designs can be conveyed through sketches, drawings, or physical models. These representations are useful for communicating ideas for a problem's solutions to other people.	• At whatever stage, communicating with peers about proposed solutions is an important part of the design process, and shared ideas can lead to improved designs.

Source: Willard, T., ed. 2015. *The NSTA quick-reference guide to the* NGSS: *Elementary school.* Arlington, VA: NSTA Press.

engage

Drum Dream Girl Read-Aloud

Connecting to the Common Core
Reading: Literature
KEY IDEAS AND DETAILS: 1.1

Inferring

Show students the cover of *Drum Dream Girl* and introduce the author and illustrator. Read the title and subtitle aloud. Then *ask*

? Based on the cover illustration and the title, what do you think this book is about? (Answers will vary.)

Next, show students the book trailer for *Drum Dream Girl* (see "Website" section). Explain that a book trailer is like a movie trailer; it gives you a preview of what the book is about. *Ask*

? Now, what do you think the book is about?

Read the subtitle of the book, *How One Girl's Courage Changed Music,* and *ask*

? What does *courage* mean? (bravery, the ability to do something you know is difficult)

 Determining Importance

Tell students that as you read the book aloud, you would like them to listen for examples of how the girl in the book showed courage and how she changed music in her country.

Then, read the book aloud, stopping periodically to ask guiding questions, such as the following:

? How do you think the girl felt when she was told only boys should play drums? (disappointed, determined)

? What evidence from the text or illustrations made you think so? (She looks disappointed in the illustrations. She never gave up.)

? Do you think it was fair that only boys were allowed to play drums? (Answers will vary.)

? What happened when the girl was able to take lessons? (She learned more and practiced a lot.)

After reading, reread the title and subtitle, *Drum Dream Girl: How One Girl's Courage Changed Music,* and *ask*

? How did the girl show courage? (She kept playing drums even though she was told girls could not play them. She practiced and practiced so that she could prove that girls can play as well as boys. She never gave up.)

? How did the girl "change music"? (She proved that girls can play drums, and from then on, girls were allowed to play drums in her country.)

Finally, read the Historical Note at the end of the book, which reveals that this is the true story of a girl named Millo Castro Zaldarriaga, and that the "island of music" in the story is Cuba. Locate Cuba on a map or globe together. Tell students that Cuba is known for its lively, rhythmic music and that drums are a big part of Cuban music.

explore

Different Drums, Different Sounds

Connecting to the Common Core
Reading: Literature
KEY IDEAS AND DETAILS: 1.1

Ask

? Can you recall the names of any of the drums from the book *Drum Dream Girl*? (congas, bongos, and timbales)

Refer to the author's descriptions of these drums: "tall conga drums, small bongo drums, and silvery moon-bright timbales." *Ask*

? Have you ever seen or heard these types of drums? (Answers will vary.)

? What other types of drums do you know of? (Answers will vary.)

EXPLORING DIFFERENT KINDS OF DRUMS

 *Making Connections: Text to Text*

If possible, bring in three or more different types of drums. The more variety in size and shape, the better. You may want to borrow them from your school music teacher, a high school band director, or a local music school. Demonstrate how to play the drums, or, better yet, invite the music teacher or a drummer to your classroom to show students how various drums look and sound. Have students listen carefully so they can observe the phenomenon that drums of different sizes and shapes make different sounds. Encourage students to describe the sounds as the drums are played. Then *ask*

? What were some differences among the drums? (They were different sizes and shapes. The drums made different sounds. Some were played with sticks, and some were played with hands.)

? How would you describe the shapes of the different drums you saw? (Answers will vary depending on the drums.)

? Do you notice a pattern in how drums are shaped? (They are usually a cylinder. They have something on top that you hit and a hollow area inside.)

? Why do you think most drums have round heads and are shaped somewhat like a cylinder? (They sound better, they can stand up on one end, etc.)

? Do you notice a pattern in how the size of the drum relates to the sound it makes? (Students should notice that larger drums typically make lower sounds, and smaller drums typically make higher sounds.)

? How do you make a drum sound louder? (Hit it harder.)

? How do you make a drum sound softer? (Hit it more lightly.)

Comparing Sounds

Next, tell students that they can make sounds similar to drums by using everyday objects that are shaped like drums. In advance, collect a variety of different-sized cylindrical containers such as metal or plastic coffee cans, popcorn canisters, cookie tins, cardboard oatmeal containers, plastic butter containers, and so on. Cover any sharp edges of metal containers with duct tape or masking tape. Be sure the containers have been cleaned, and confirm that there were no food allergens contained in them previously (e.g., do not use peanut butter containers or tree nut tins). Tell students that they are going to use these containers as models of (headless) drums, and you would like them to compare the different sounds the models make when they are struck. Give each student one of the containers and a drumstick, chopstick, dowel rod, wooden spoon, or pencil. Have them tap their containers in different places and notice the different sounds. Next, call on two students with two different containers and compare the shapes of the containers using words such as *bigger, smaller, shorter, taller, wider,* and *narrower*. Then, have students tap the containers and compare the sounds they make, using words such as *louder, softer, lower,* and *higher* when comparing the sounds. Repeat with different pairs of students and their drums so that students can observe how the shape and size of the container affect the sounds they make. *Ask*

? What did you notice? (Answers will vary.)

? What do you wonder? (Answers will vary.)

Then reread the pages from *Drum Dream Girl* that describe how she played rhythms: "At home,

her fingertips rolled out their own dreamy drum **rhythm** on tables and chairs," and "Her hands seemed to fly as they rippled, rapped, and pounded all the **rhythms** of her drum dreams." *Ask*

? What do you think it means to play rhythms? (Answers will vary.)

Teach students a simple rhythm. Practice the rhythm in unison several times, with each student playing his or her own container. Then tell students that you would like them to play the rhythm on their containers in turn. Everyone else should be silent and listen to the sound each type of container makes.

Afterward, collect the materials, and *ask*

? After playing some rhythms together, what do you think the word *rhythm* means? (Answers will vary.)

? Did all of the containers sound the same when you hit them? (no)

? What was different about the sounds? (Some were loud, some soft, some high, some low, etc.)

? Why do you think each container sounded different? (Answers will vary.)

explain

Drum Sounds Article

> Connecting to the Common Core
> **Reading: Informational Text**
> KEY IDEAS AND DETAILS: 1.1

Before reading the article together, *ask*

? What are the parts of a drum? (Answers will vary.)

? How does a drum make sound? (Answers will vary.)

? What do you think a rhythm is? (Answers will vary.)

? What is the difference between making noise with a drum and making music with a drum? (Answers will vary.)

> **SEP: Obtaining, Evaluating, and Communicating Information**
> Read grade-appropriate texts and/or use media to obtain scientific and/or technical information to determine patterns in and/or evidence about the natural and designed world(s).

Tell students that you have an article that will help them learn the answers to these and other questions about drums.

 Stop and Try It

Give each student a copy of the Drums Sounds student page. Have students follow along as you read the article aloud. Stop at the end of each section, and do the Stop-and-Try-It activities together. Below are the instructions for each Stop-and-Try-It activity and some explanations for you to adapt and share with students.

Parts of a Drum Activity

Identify the head, rim, and shell on a drum. Listen closely as each part is hit with a drumstick, and compare the sounds that are made. *Ask*

? Why do you think the sound is different when you hit the drumstick on the head, rim, and shell? (Those parts are made of different materials and are different sizes and shapes.)

Explanation: Students should be able to identify the three parts of a drum on several different drums and hear the different sounds made by hitting the head, rim, and shell. Although most of the drumming occurs on the head of the drum, drummers will sometimes strike the rim or shell to get a different sound.

Have students recall the different shapes of the drums from the book *Drum Dream Girl* and the Different Drums, Different Sounds activity (conga: cylinder or barrel shape; bongo: cylinder or "cut-off-cone" shape; timbale: cylinder shape). Draw both a cylinder and a truncated cone on the board. Tell students that most drums are shaped roughly like a cylinder or cut-off cone because those shapes help the sound reverberate, or bounce around, inside the drum better when you hit the drumhead. It is also easier to stretch a drumhead evenly over a round shape as opposed to a rectangular or irregular shape. However, there are bowl-shaped drums such as timpani, and there is even a drum shaped like a box (rectangular prism) that is played with the drummer sitting on top of it!

OBSERVING SOUND MAKING OBJECTS VIBRATE

How Drums Make Sound Activity

You can't see sound vibrations, but you can see how sound makes objects vibrate. Cover a bowl tightly with plastic wrap. Sprinkle some grains of rice on the plastic wrap. Observe the rice as a drum is hit near, but not touching, the bowl. What happens when the drum is hit harder? (*Note:* A large, sturdy bowl will work best. Be sure the plastic wrap is stretched tightly and secured around the opening of the bowl, using tape or a large rubber band. A teaspoon of dry rice sprinkled on top should be sufficient.)

Explanation: Students should notice that the grains of rice vibrate even when the drum does not touch the plastic wrap or bowl. They vibrate more when the drum is hit harder and less when the drum is hit more softly. Explain to students that the sound vibrations are traveling through the air and making the plastic wrap vibrate, which causes the rice grains to move. Students may also notice that because the rice grains are moving, they are also making a faint sound.

How Drums Make Music Activity

Try tapping out the rhythm of a simple nursery rhyme with a pencil on your desk, such as "Hickory Dickory Dock" (Hick/o/ry Dick/o/ry Dock). Now, create your own rhythm and teach it to a partner. Play the rhythm together. You're making music!

Explanation: Banging on drums can sound quite noisy and chaotic, but when you play a rhythm on a drum, it becomes music. Explain that a rhythm is a repeating pattern and it can be simple or complex. Grab a drum or container and demonstrate a simple pattern such as Hick/o/ry Dick/o/ry Dock. Repeat the pattern several times and have students play along. Explain that adding simple patterns together creates a rhythm. Then demonstrate a rhythm that is a little more complicated, and have students repeat it. Next, allow students to come up with their own rhythm on a drum or container, and teach it to a partner or the class. Finally, explain that because a rhythm is a repeated pattern, or patterns added together, rhythm actually involves mathematics. In fact, there are many connections between music and math. Tell students that researchers have even discovered that learning to play music might help kids do better in math!

elaborate

Drum City Read-Aloud

> Connecting to the Common Core
> **Reading: Literature**
> KEY IDEAS AND DETAILS: 1.1

Determining Importance

Show students the cover of *Drum City* and introduce the author and illustrator. Tell students to look closely at the cover illustration, and then *ask*

? What do you think this book might be about? (Students will likely notice the kids on the cover banging on homemade drums and marching in a parade.)

Tell students that as you read the book aloud, you would like them to look and listen for all the different types of homemade drums the children use in the book. Read the book aloud, being sure to demonstrate the intended rhythm of the book by emphasizing the words set in larger print.

DESIGNING DRUMS

Design a Drum

Ask

? Now that you know how drums make sound, can you design a drum using things at home or in our classroom?

> **SEP: Constructing Explanations and Designing Solutions**
> Use tools and/or materials to design and/or build a device that solves a specific problem or solution to a specific problem.

Tell students that they are going to have the opportunity to design their own drums. Students can use a container from the *explore* phase of the lesson as the shell of their drums. Provide a variety of different materials from which students can make drumheads, such as duct tape, packing tape, shrink wrap, or large balloons. Make sure they stretch their drumheads across the opening of the containers as tightly and as evenly as possible to ensure the best sound. They can use tape or rubber bands to fasten the head to the rim of the drum. Allow students time to tinker with the various supplies to make a drum that sounds the way they want it to sound. Provide supplies for them to make drumsticks, too, such as dowel rods, chopsticks, wooden spoons, or pencils. If desired, students can wrap duct tape on the ends to make them look more like drumsticks. Encourage students to experiment with changing the sounds of their drums by using different sizes of cylinders and by stretching different materials across the opening to make the drumheads. When they are satisfied with their drum designs, they can cover the shells of their drums with construction paper and decorate them with markers, crayons, stickers, colorful duct tape, glitter, and so on.

If you prefer to have students design and build their drums at home, you can send home the Design a Drum student page, copied front-to-back with the My Drum Design student page. Be sure to have them write in the due date at the bottom.

evaluate

My Drum Design

Connecting to the Common Core
Writing
RESEARCH TO BUILD AND PRESENT KNOWLEDGE: 1.8

> **SEP: Obtaining, Evaluating, and Communicating Information**
> Communicate information or design ideas and/or solutions with others in oral and/or written forms using models, drawings, writing, or numbers that provide detail about scientific ideas, practices, and/or design ideas.

Writing

Give each student a copy of the My Drum Design student page. Have students sketch their drum and label the head, rim, and shell. They will also list the materials they used and explain why they chose those materials. Finally, they will explain how their drum makes sound using the word *vibrates, vibrating,* or *vibration.* For example, "My drum makes sound by *vibrating* when I strike the head with a wooden spoon."

Turn and Talk

When students finish designing their drums, have each student find a partner and turn and talk. They can compare the materials they used and the sounds their drums make. Next, allow them to demonstrate

COMPARING OUR DRUMS

the sounds for the class. They should explain what they used for the head and the shell and how they made the drumsticks (if applicable). Students can demonstrate the unique sound of their drums by playing a short rhythm for the class. For fun, your students could parade through your school or playground, just like the children did in the book *Drum City,* who all play the same rhythm on their drums as they march along.

STEM Everywhere

Give students the STEM Everywhere student page as a way to involve their families and extend their learning. They can do the activity with an adult helper and share their results with the class. If students do not have access to the materials (or the internet) at home, you may choose to have them complete this activity at school.

Opportunities for Differentiated Instruction

This box lists questions and challenges related to the lesson that students may select to research, investigate, or innovate. Students may also use the questions as examples to help them generate their own questions. These questions can help you move your students from the teacher-directed investigation to engaging in the science and engineering practices in a more student-directed format.

Extra Support

For students who are struggling to meet the lesson objectives, provide a question and guide them in the process of collecting research or helping them design procedures or solutions.

Extensions

For students with high interest or who have already met the lesson objectives, have them choose a question (or pose their own question), conduct their own research, and design their own procedures or solutions.

After selecting one of the questions in this box or formulating their own questions, students can individually or collaboratively make predictions, design investigations or surveys to test their predictions, collect evidence, devise explanations, design solutions, or examine related resources. They can communicate their findings through a science notebook, at a poster session or gallery walk, or by producing a media project.

Research

Have students brainstorm researchable questions:

? What were the first drums made of?

? What are some other types of drums from around the world?

? How do string instruments make sound?

Investigate

Have students brainstorm testable questions to be solved through science or math:

? Can sounds travel underwater?

? Can sounds travel through solids?

? What materials muffle sound the best?

Innovate

Have students brainstorm problems to be solved through engineering:

? What could you design to carry your drum as you play it?

? How can you build a rubber band guitar that plays different notes?

? How can you build a cup-and-string telephone to talk to a friend across the room?

Website

Drum Dream Girl (book trailer)
www.youtube.com/watch?v=_
IruQabrUco

More Books to Read

Boothroyd, J. 2011. *Loud or soft? High or low? A look at sound.* Minneapolis: Lerner.

Summary: Part of the *Lightning Bolt Books* series, this book provides a simple introduction to sound—how sounds are made, how they travel, and how sounds compare.

Brown, M. 2013. *Tito Puente, mambo king/Tito Puente, rey del mambo.* New York: HarperCollins.

Summary: This biography of legendary musician Tito Puente is written in both English and Spanish. Author Monica Brown's engaging text and Raphael Lopez's vibrant illustrations tell the remarkable true story of how a young boy's love of music turned him into the Mambo King!

Perkins, A. 1969. *Hand, hand, fingers, thumb.* New York: Random House.

Summary: This classic *Bright and Early Book for Beginning Readers* features lovable "monkeys" (chimpanzees, actually) who play a variety of drums with their hands, fingers, and thumbs. Readers will find themselves tapping out the infectious rhythms of the book: "Hand, hand, fingers thumb. One thumb, one thumb, drumming on a drum. One hand, two hands, drumming on a drum. Dum ditty, dum ditty, dum dum dum."

Pinkney, B. 1994. *Max found two sticks.* New York: Simon & Schuster Books for Young Readers.

Summary: Max doesn't feel like talking to anyone, but when he sees two heavy twigs fall to the ground, he picks them up and begins tapping out the rhythms of everything he sees and hears around him—the sound of pigeons startled into flight, rain against the windows, distant church bells, and the rumble of a subway. Then, when a marching band rounds Max's corner, something wonderful happens.

Name: _____

Drum Sounds

Since the beginning of history, people have been making and playing drums. There are many different kinds of drums, but they all work in the same basic way.

Parts of a Drum

A drum typically has three basic parts: head, rim, and shell. The **head** is the part you hit with your hand or a drumstick. The first drumheads were made out of animal skin, but now they are usually made from some kind of plastic. The **rim** is the edge around the head. Drummers can play the rim of the drum to get a sound that is different from playing on the head. The **shell** is the base of the drum. The size, shape, and material of the shell affect the sound of the drum. Most drum shells are wooden, roughly the shape of a **cylinder,** and hollow inside.

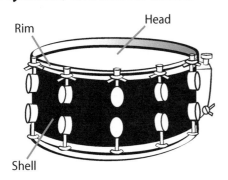

Rim Head

Shell

STOP and TRY IT: Identify the head, rim, and shell on a drum. Listen closely as each part is hit with a drumstick, and compare the sounds that are made.

How Drums Make Sound

When you hit a drum, the drumhead **vibrates**, or moves back and forth very quickly. These **vibrations** create sound waves that travel through the air in all directions. When they reach your ears, you hear the sound made by the drum. All sounds are caused by vibrations.

STOP and TRY IT: You can't see sound vibrations, but you can see how sound makes objects vibrate. Cover a bowl tightly with plastic wrap. Sprinkle some grains of rice on the plastic wrap. Observe the rice as a drum is hit near, but not touching, the bowl. What happens when the drum is hit harder?

How Drums Make Music

Banging on a drum might just sound like noise. In order to make music with a drum, you play a **rhythm**. A rhythm is a repeated pattern of sounds.

STOP and TRY IT: Try tapping out the rhythm of a simple nursery rhyme with a pencil on your desk, such as "Hickory Dickory Dock" (Hick/o/ry Dick/o/ry Dock) Now, create your own rhythm and teach it to a partner. Play the rhythm together. You're making music!

National Science Teaching Association

Design a Drum

Dear _____,

We have been learning about drums during a STEM unit on sound. We have studied the parts of a drum, how drums make sound through **vibration**, and how different kinds of drums produce different sounds. Your learner will be designing and building their own drum by following the directions below.

Directions

1. Choose a clean cylinder-shaped container for the shell of the drum, such as a coffee can, a cookie tin, or an oatmeal container. Remove the lid from the container, and cover any sharp edges with duct tape or masking tape.

2. Test different materials for the drumhead. You can try duct tape, packing tape, shrink wrap, or even a large balloon.

3. Make the drumhead by taping or stretching the material tightly over the rim of the container. You may need to use large rubber bands to hold the material in place.

4. Tape or glue construction paper around your drum to completely cover the shell.

5. Decorate the paper with markers, crayons, stickers, colorful duct tape, glitter, or other materials.

6. Test different objects to use for drumsticks. Dowel rods, chopsticks, pencils, or wooden spoons will do.

7. Play your drum! Practice creating simple patterns of sound, or **rhythms**, on your drum.

Drums are due on_____.

Name: _____

My Drum Design

Sketch your drum in the box below and label the **head, rim,** and **shell.**

```
┌────────────────────────────────────────┐
│                                          │
│                                          │
│                                          │
│                                          │
│                                          │
│                                          │
│                                          │
└────────────────────────────────────────┘
```

1. What materials did you use to make your drum?

_____

_____

_____

2. Why did you choose those materials?

_____

_____

_____

3. How does your drum make sound? Use the word **vibrates, vibrating,** or **vibration** in your explanation.

_____

_____

National Science Teaching Association

Name: _____

STEM Everywhere

Dear Families,

At school, we have been learning about how **drums make sound.** We have studied the parts of a drum, how they make sound through vibrations, and how rhythms can be played on drums. To find out more, ask your learner the following questions and discuss their answers:

What did you learn?

What was your favorite part of the lesson?

What are you still wondering?

 At home, you can watch a video together called "STOMP," which is about using everyday objects to make patterns of sound that turn noise into music. To watch the video, scan the QR code, go to *www. pbslearningmedia.org* and search for "STOMP," or go to *www. pbslearningmedia.org/resource/vtl07.math.algebra.pat.stomp/stomp-cyberchase*.

After you watch the video, look around the house to find objects you can use to create rhythms. You can even invite friends and family to join in! Draw or write how you made rhythms below.

Object	How We Used It to Create Rhythms